PRO[LOGUE]

IN A DISTANT AND SECO[ND-HAND SET OF DIMENSIONS...]

IN AN ASTRAL PLANE THAT WAS **NEVER** MEANT TO FLY...

SEE...

...**GREAT A 'TUIN THE TURTLE** COMES, SWIMMING THROUGH THE INTERSTELLAR GULF.

THROUGH SEA-SIZED EYES, HE STARES FIXEDLY AT THE **DESTINATION.**

IN A BRAIN BIGGER THAN A CITY, HE THINKS ONLY OF THE **WEIGHT.**

MOST OF THE WEIGHT IS, OF COURSE, ACCOUNTED FOR BY BERILIA, TUBUL, GREAT T'PHON, AND JERAKEEN, ON WHOSE STAR-TANNED SHOULDERS THE *DISC* OF THE WORLD RESTS.

THE DISC IS GARLANDED BY THE LONG *WATERFALL* AT ITS VAST CIRCUMFERENCE AND DOOMED BY THE BABY BLUE VAULT OF *HEAVEN*.

ASTROPSYCHOLOGY HAS BEEN, AS YET, *UNABLE* TO ESTABLISH WHAT *THEY* THINK ABOUT.

THE GREAT TURTLE WAS A MERE *HYPOTHESIS*... UNTIL THE DAY THE SMALL AND SECRETIVE KINGDOM OF *KRULL* LOWERED SEVERAL OBSERVERS OVER THE EDGE--

--TO *PEER* THROUGH THE MIST VEILS.

THE EARLY *ASTROZOOLOGISTS* WERE ABLE TO BRING BACK MUCH INFORMATION ABOUT THE SHAPE AND NATURE OF A'TUIN AND THE ELEPHANTS--

--BUT THIS DID *NOT* RESOLVE THE FUNDAMENTAL QUESTIONS ABOUT THE NATURE AND *PURPOSE* OF THE UNIVERSE...

...FOR EXAMPLE, WHAT WAS A'TUIN'S ACTUAL *SEX* ?

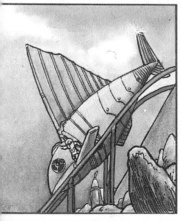

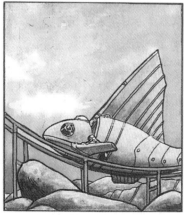

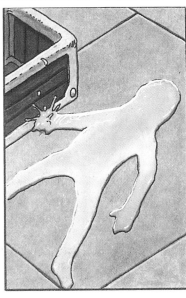

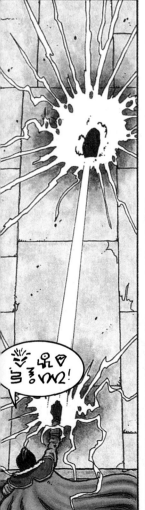

MAGICIANS! WHERE ARE MY MAGICIANS!?!

WE'RE TOTALLY *LOST* IN A PALACE ON AN ISLAND WE *HAVEN'T* A HOPE OF LEAVING...

--WHAT'S *MORE*, WE... HEY!

FANTASTIC!

I THOUGHT FATE DIDN'T GO IN FOR BARGAINING. I THOUGHT FATE WAS IMPLACABLE.

NORMALLY, YES, BUT YOU TWO HAVE BEEN THORNS IN HIS SIDE FOR SOME TIME. HE SPECIFIED THAT THE SACRIFICES SHOULD BE YOU.

HE ALLOWED YOU TO ESCAPE FROM THE PIRATES, HE ALLOWED YOU TO DRIFT INTO THE CIRCUMFENCE. FATE CAN BE ONE MEAN GOD AT TIMES.

BUT YOU CAN HELP US?

YOU AMUSE ME, I HAVE A SENTIMENTAL STREAK. YOU'D KNOW THAT IF YOU WERE GAMBLERS.

FOR A WHILE I RODE IN A FROG'S MIND, AND YOU KINDLY RESCUED ME.

THE WHOLE MIND OF FATE IS BENT AGAINST YOU. ALL I CAN DO IS GIVE YOU ONE CHANCE.

JUST ONE SMALL CHANCE, THE REST IS UP TO YOU.

GOSH.

AH, YOU ARE READY, I SEE.

READY.

POP!

KKRRSSHH!

WHEN ARE YOU COMING DOWN?

I DON'T KNOW. HE USED ATAVARR'S PERSONAL GRAVITATIONAL UPSET. UNTIL IT *WEARS OFF*, MY BODY IS CONVINCED THAT *"DOWN"* LIES 90 DEGREES TO THE *NORMAL* DIRECTION.

WHY DON'T YOU *EVER* WORRY? WE'RE GOING TO BE SACRIFICED IN THE MORNING, AND YOU *JUST* SIT THERE EATING *BARNACLE* CANAPES!

I MEAN IT'S NOT AS IF WE KNOW *WHY* WE'RE GOING TO BE KILLED!

YOU'D LIKE TO, WOULD YOU?

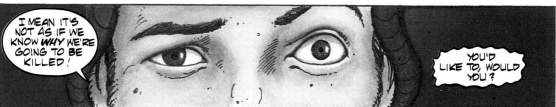

DID *YOU* SAY THAT?

SAY *WHAT*?

YOU'RE *HEARING* THINGS.

IT'S HAPPENED AT LAST. I'M GOING *OUT OF* MY *MIND*.

GOOD IDEA. IT'S PRETTY *CROWDED* IN HERE.

POP!

IT *DAWNED* ON RINCEWIND--VERY SLOWLY, BECAUSE IT WAS A COMPLETELY *NEW* SENSATION--THAT SOMEONE IN THE WORLD WAS *FRIGHTENED* OF HIM.

WHAT IS YOUR *NAME*?

MY NAME IS *IMMATERIAL*.

THAT'S A *PRETTY* NAME.

IF I HAD A WAND LIKE *THAT*, I WOULDN'T BE FRIGHTENED OF ANYTHING. SO *WHAT* IN CREATION CAN SHE IMAGINE I COULD DO?

DON'T *MOCK* ME. MY NAME IS MARCHESA, AND I AM A WIZARD OF THE *FIFTH LEVEL*.

I MUST BRING YOU *ALIVE*, BUT NO ONE SAID ANYTHING ABOUT BRINGING YOU TO KRULL *WHOLE*, UNDERSTAND?

SINCE YOU KNOW ALL ABOUT *ME*, YOU MUST KNOW THAT I'M *NOT* EVEN A WIZARD. JUST A WIZARD OF *SORTS*.

YOU CAN'T DO MAGIC BECAUSE ONE OF THE *EIGHT GREAT SPELLS* IS LODGED IN YOUR MIND. THAT'S WHY YOU WERE *THROWN OUT* OF THE UNSEEN UNIVERSITY. WE KNOW.

BUT YOU SAID HE WAS A MAGICIAN OF GREAT *CUNNING* AND ARTIFICE.

YES, BECAUSE ANYONE WHO HAS *SURVIVED* ALL THAT HE HAS MUST BE *SOME* KIND OF MAGICIAN.

I *WARN* YOU, RINCEWIND. IF YOU GIVE ME THE MEREST SUSPICION THAT YOU ARE INTONING THE *GREAT SPELL*, I WILL *KILL* YOU.

I HOPE YOU'RE NOT PROPOSING TO *ENSLAVE* US.

CERTAINLY *NOT*! YOUR LIVES IN KRULL WILL BE *RICH, FULL,* AND *COMFORTABLE*--

--JUST NOT VERY LONG.

OH, GOOD!

HAD EITHER OF THEM **LOOKED DOWN** AT THAT MOMENT, THEY WOULD HAVE SEEN THE V-SHAPED **WAVE** SURGING DIRECTLY TOWARD TETHIS' ISLAND.

BUT THEY **WEREN'T** LOOKING.

WE'RE *IMPORTANT*, NO LIE. THEY WOULDN'T BE *WASTING* ALL THAT MAGIC ON A COUPLE OF POTENTIAL SLAVES.

WHAT IS IT?

" WELL, THE *DISC* ITSELF WOULD HAVE BEEN CREATED BY FRESNEL'S WONDERFUL CONCENTRATOR. IT TAKES *EIGHT* FOURTH-GRADE WIZARDS A *WEEK* TO ENVISION.

" THEN THERE'S THOSE *WIZARDS* ON IT, WHO MUST ALL BE GIFTED *HYDROPHOBES*... "

" A REALLY *GOOD* HYDRO-PHOBE HAS TO BE TRAINED ON *DEHYDRATED* WATER FROM BIRTH. THAT COSTS A *FORTUNE* IN MAGIC ALONE.

YOU MEAN THEY *HATE* WATER?

NO, HATE IS AN *ATTRACTING* FORCE, JUST LIKE LOVE. THEY REALLY *LOATHE* IT, THE VERY IDEA REVOLTS THEM.

" BUT THEY MAKE GREAT *WEATHER* MAGICIANS. RAIN CLOUDS JUST *GIVE UP* AND GO AWAY.

IT SOUNDS *TERRIBLE*

AND THEY ALL *DIE* YOUNG. THEY JUST *CAN'T LIVE* WITH THEM-SELVES.

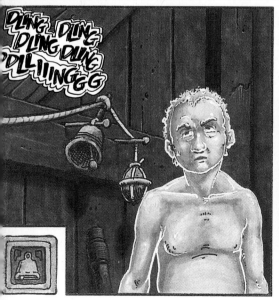

ARE YOU **AWAKE**?

I **SAID**, ARE YOU AWAKE? IT'S NEARLY **DAWN**, AND WE'VE GOT TO GET OUT OF HERE **BEFORE** THE SALVAGE FLEET COMES!

SCRDFNGH.

LOOK, THERE'S ALL KINDS OF **WEAPONS** AND STUFF IN HERE. WHEN TETHIS COMES BACK WE COULD **OVERPOWER** HIM.

THAT'S A BIT **UNGRACIOUS**, ISN'T IT?

TOUGH BUNS. THIS IS A **ROUGH** UNIVERSE.

UNNGGHH!

WOULD HE **LEAVE** THAT SORT OF THING AROUND IF IT COULD **HURT** HIM?

SHHH! **HE'S COMING!**

THUNK!

≥SIGH≤ IT **WOULDN'T** HAVE HARMED ME, BUT NEVERTHELESS, I **AM** HURT. **DEEPLY** HURT.

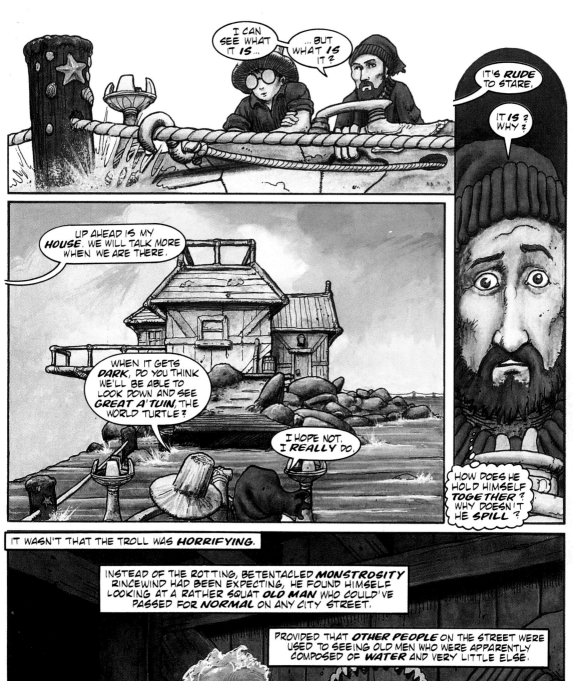

I CAN SEE WHAT IT *IS*...

...BUT WHAT *IS* IT?

IT'S *RUDE* TO STARE.

IT *IS*? WHY?

UP AHEAD IS MY *HOUSE*. WE WILL TALK MORE WHEN WE ARE THERE.

WHEN IT GETS *DARK*, DO YOU THINK WE'LL BE ABLE TO LOOK DOWN AND SEE *GREAT A'TUIN*, THE WORLD TURTLE?

I HOPE NOT. I *REALLY* DO.

HOW DOES HE HOLD HIMSELF *TOGETHER*? WHY DOESN'T HE *SPILL*?

IT WASN'T THAT THE TROLL WAS *HORRIFYING*.

INSTEAD OF THE ROTTING, BETENTACLED *MONSTROSITY* RINCEWIND HAD BEEN EXPECTING, HE FOUND HIMSELF LOOKING AT A RATHER SQUAT *OLD MAN* WHO COULD'VE PASSED FOR *NORMAL* ON ANY CITY STREET.

PROVIDED THAT *OTHER PEOPLE* ON THE STREET WERE USED TO SEEING OLD MEN WHO WERE APPARENTLY COMPOSED OF *WATER* AND VERY LITTLE ELSE.

IT WAS AS IF THE *OCEAN* HAD DECIDED TO CREATE *LIFE* WITHOUT GOING THROUGH ALL THAT *TEDIOUS* BUSINESS OF EVOLUTION...

...AND HAD SIMPLY FORMED A *PART* OF *ITSELF* INTO A BIPED AND SENT IT WALKING *SQUISHILY* UP THE BEACH.

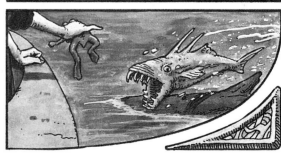

Next: CLOSE TO THE EDGE.

KILL THEM!

KILLING **UNCONSCIOUS** PEOPLE ISN'T RIGHT.

I CAN'T THINK OF A MORE **OPPORTUNE** TIME.

THEN I SHALL **BANISH** THEM. ONCE THEY ARE BEYOND THE WYRMBERG'S MAGIC, THEY'LL HAVE **NO** POWER.

WHAT'S THE NEXT **TEST**, THEN?

I WARN YOU THAT IT IS **PERILOUS**. IF YOU WISH, YOU MAY **LEAVE** NOW.

AM I TO BE **WEAPONLESS** AGAIN?

I THINK **NOT**.

I WAS **VERY GOOD** AT IT WHEN I WAS **ALIVE.** I COULD IMAGINE UP TO, OH, **FIVE HUNDRED DRAGONS** AT ONE TIME.

NOW LIESSA, THE MOST **SKILLED** OF MY CHILDREN, CAN BARELY IMAGINE **FIFTY.** SHE DOESN'T **REALLY BELIEVE** IN THEM.

THAT'S WHY HERS ARE RATHER **BORING**-- WHILE YOURS IS ALMOST AS GOOD AS SOME OF **MINE** USED TO BE.

THE DEAD DON'T, ER, YOU KNOW... **TALK** MUCH. AS A RULE.

I USED TO BE A POWERFUL **WIZARD.** MY DAUGHTER POISONED ME. BUT--

--IT SOON BECAME OBVIOUS THAT **NONE** OF MY THREE CHILDREN IS SUFFICIENTLY POWERFUL TO REST THE LORDSHIP FROM THE OTHERS.

MOST **UNSATISFACTORY.** SO I RESOLVED TO REMAIN ALIVE IN AN **UNOFFICIAL** CAPACITY.

LIESSA **KIDNAPPED** US?

HER POWER IS **STRONGEST.** MY SONS ARE INCAPABLE OF FLYING MORE THAN A FEW **MILES** BEFORE THEY FADE.

I DID **NOTICE** THAT WE COULD SEE THROUGH THEM. I THOUGHT THAT WAS **ODD.**

THE POWER ONLY **WORKS** NEAR THE WYRMBERG. IT'S THE **INVERSE SQUARE** LAW, YOU KNOW.

BUT I EXPECT YOU'LL BE WANTING TO **RESCUE YOUR FRIEND...**

HRUN?

NOT **HIM.** THE SKINNY WIZARD. MY SON LIO!RT IS TRYING TO **HACK** HIM TO PIECES.

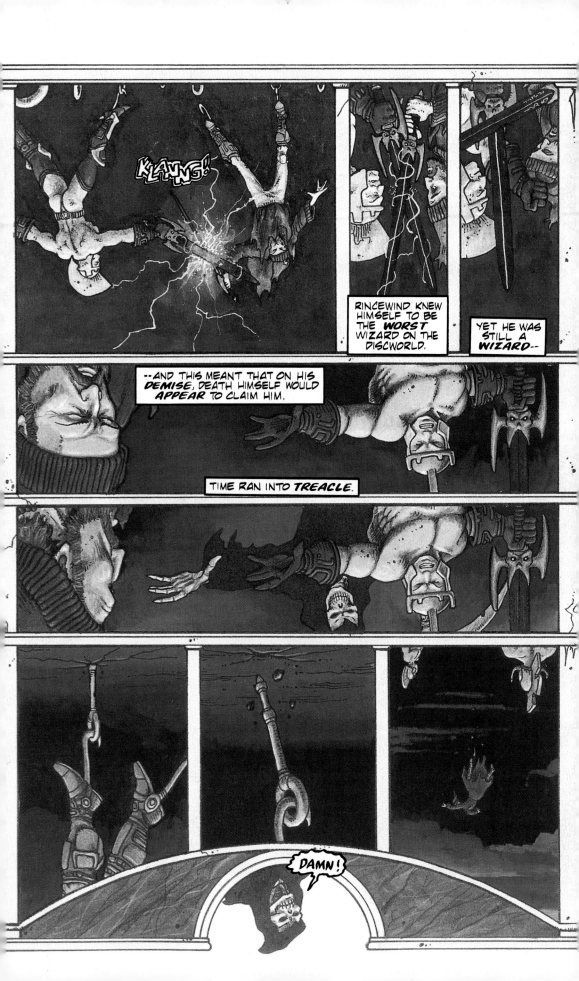

HUH?

TELL THE DRAGON THAT IF IT *SINGES* ME, I'LL LET THE SWORD GO! I WILL! I'LL LET IT *GO*!

WHERE ARE MY *FRIENDS*? THE BARBARIAN AND THE LITTLE MAN, I MEAN!

I EXPECT THEY'VE BEEN TAKEN TO THE *WYRMBERG*.

RIGHT, THEN. YOU'D BETTER TAKE *ME* THERE.

I WAS SUPPOSED TO TAKE YOU IN *DEAD*.

IF WE'RE TALKING ABOUT *ANYBODY* BEING DEAD, REMEMBER WHOSE *SWORD* IS IN WHICH HAND.

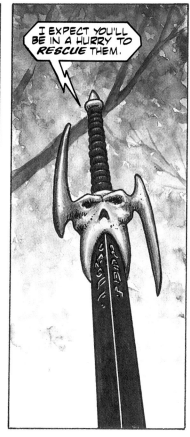

MAGIC NEVER DIES, IT MERELY *FADES* AWAY.

NOWHERE IS THAT MORE *EVIDENT* THAN IN THOSE AREAS THAT HAD BEEN THE SCENES OF THE GREAT BATTLES OF THE *MAGE WARS.*

IN THOSE DAYS, MAGIC IN ITS *RAW STATE* HAD BEEN WIDELY *AVAILABLE* AND EAGERLY UTILISED.

DISC PHILOSOPHERS AGREE THAT THE *FIRST MEN*, SHORTLY AFTER THEIR CREATION, UNDERSTANDABLY *LOST* THEIR TEMPERS.

THE SUN WHEELED *ACROSS* THE SKY, THE SEAS BOILED, SMALL WHITE *DOVES* APPEARED IN PEOPLE'S CLOTHING.

THE VERY *STABILITY* OF THE DISC WAS THREATENED.

THIS RESULTED IN STERN ACTION BY THE *OLD HIGH ONES*, TO WHOM EVEN THE GODS WERE *ANSWERABLE.*

THE GODS WERE *BANISHED* TO THE HIGH PLACES, AND MEN WERE *RECREATED* A GOOD DEAL SMALLER.

MUCH OF THE OLD, WILD MAGIC WAS *SUCKED OUT* OF THE EARTH.

THAT DID NOT SOLVE THE *PROBLEM* OF THOSE PLACES THAT HAD SUFFERED A *DIRECT HIT* BY A SPELL.

THE MAGIC FADED AWAY *SLOWLY*, SEVERELY DISTORTING THE *REALITY* AROUND IT.

IT WAS CALLED THE *WYRMBERG.*

AT IT'S BASE IT WAS A MERE SCORE OF *YARDS* ACROSS.

THEN IT ROSE THROUGH CLINGING CLOUD UNTIL IT WAS TRUNCATED BY A PLATEAU FULLY A *QUARTER OF A MILE* ACROSS.

THE *CAVE MOUTHS* IN ITS SIDE HAD A CRUDELY CARVED, REGULAR LOOK ABOUT THEM, SO THAT THE WYRMBERG HUNG OVER THE CLOUDS LIKE A *GIANT'S DOVECOTE.*

THAT WOULD MEAN THE "*DOVES*" HAD A WINGSPAN SLIGHTLY IN EXCESS OF *FORTY YARDS.*

The Lure of the Wyrm

BASED ON THE NOVEL BY:
TERRY PRATCHETT
ADAPTED BY:
SCOTT ROCKWELL
ART BY:
STEVEN ROSS
LETTERED BY:
VICKIE WILLIAMS
EDITED BY:
DAVID CAMPITI

NEXT : *THE LURE OF THE WYRM!*

IMPRESSIVE, ISN'T IT?

SOMETIME LATER, IN THE MOORLAND IMWARDS OF THE FORMER TEMPLE...

...AND THEN I BELONGED TO THE PASHA OF RE'DURAT AND PLAYED A PROMINENT PART IN THE BATTLE OF GREAT NEF, WHERE I RECEIVED THE SLIGHT NICK YOU MAY HAVE NOTICED TWO-THIRDS OF THE WAY UP MY BLADE...

I WONDER HOW TRUSTWORTHY HRUN WILL BE. HERE IN THE WILDS, WITH TROLLS ABOUT.

...SOME INFIDEL WAS WEARING AN OCTARINE COLLAR, MOST UNSPORTING. AM I BORING YOU?

HUH? OH, NO... IT'S ALL VERY INTERESTING.

RINCEWIND!

I COULD SEE YOU WERE A CULTURED PERSON. WHAT I'D REALLY LIKE TO BE IS A PLOUGHSHARE. I DON'T KNOW WHAT IT IS, BUT IT SOUNDS LIKE AN EXISTENCE WITH SOME POINT TO IT...

THEY'RE ABOUT RIDE NOW--CAN'T HOLD THEM ANY LONGER, EVERYBODY SMILE!

AAAAOOOORRROOOOOAAAARRRRRGGHHHHH!!!!

RINCEWIND! YOUR *SPELL*!

AT THE UNSEEN UNIVERSITY WAS KEPT THE *OCTAVO*, GREATEST OF ALL GRIMOIRES, FORMERLY OWNED BY THE CREATOR OF THE UNIVERSE.

IT WAS THIS BOOK THAT RINCEWIND HAD ONCE *OPENED* FOR A BET.

ONE *SPELL* FROM THE BOOK HAD LEAPT FROM THE PAGE AND *SETTLED* IN HIS MIND LIKE A TOAD ON A STONE.

NO ONE KNOWS WHAT THE SPELL *DOES*. IT MIGHT STOP THE UNIVERSE OR END TIME.

--GAKK!

WE'RE *DOOMED.* I TELL YOU, THIS PLACE IS A SPIDERWEB. IT DOESN'T MATTER WHICH WAY WE GO, WE'LL END UP AT THE *CENTER.*

IT WAS KIND OF YOU TO COME *LOOKING* FOR ME, ANYWAY. HOW DID YOU MANAGE IT? IT WAS VERY IMPRESSIVE.

OH, WELL, I JUST THOUGHT, "I CAN'T *LEAVE* OLD TWOFLOWER THERE.."

SO WHAT WE'VE GOT TO DO NOW IS *FIND* THIS BEL-SHAMHARATH PERSON AND *EXPLAIN* THINGS TO HIM AND PERHAPS HE'LL LET US OUT.

FIND BEL-SHAMHAROTH?

WE DON'T HAVE TO GET *INVOLVED.*

FIND THE SOUL RENDER AND NOT GET INVOLVED?! JUST GIVE HIM A NOD AND ASK THE WAY TO THE EXIT?

EXPLAIN THINGS TO THE SENDER OF EIGNNNNHHH--

THE PHRASE *"SLIVER OF A SCREAM"* COMES TO MIND...

POP!!!

UNNGGHHH!

HRUN'S SWORD, *KRING,* WAS FORGED FROM A THUNDERBOLT AND HAS A SOUL, BUT SUFFERS NO SCABBARD.

HRUN HAD STOLEN IT ONLY THREE DAYS BEFORE, AND WAS ALREADY BEGINNING TO *REGRET* IT.

I TELL YOU IT WENT DOWN THAT *PASSAGE* ON THE RIGHT.

BE SILENT!

HRUN'S EARLIER *CONFUSION* WAS GONE. THIS WAS OBVIOUSLY A MAGICAL TEMPLE, AND THAT EXPLAINED EVERYTHING.

IT EXPLAINED WHY, EARLIER THIS AFTERNOON, HE HAD ESPIED A *CHEST* BY THE SIDE OF THE TRACK. IT'S TOP WAS INVITINGLY OPEN, DISPLAYING MUCH GOLD.

BUT WHEN HE HAD APPROACHED IT, IT HAD SPROUTED *LEGS* AND RUN OFF INTO THE FOREST, STOPPING A FEW HUNDRED YARDS AWAY.

ALL I SAID WAS...

SHUT UP!

NOW, AFTER SEVERAL HOURS OF TEASING PURSUIT, HE HAD LOST IT IN THESE HELL-LIT TUNNELS.

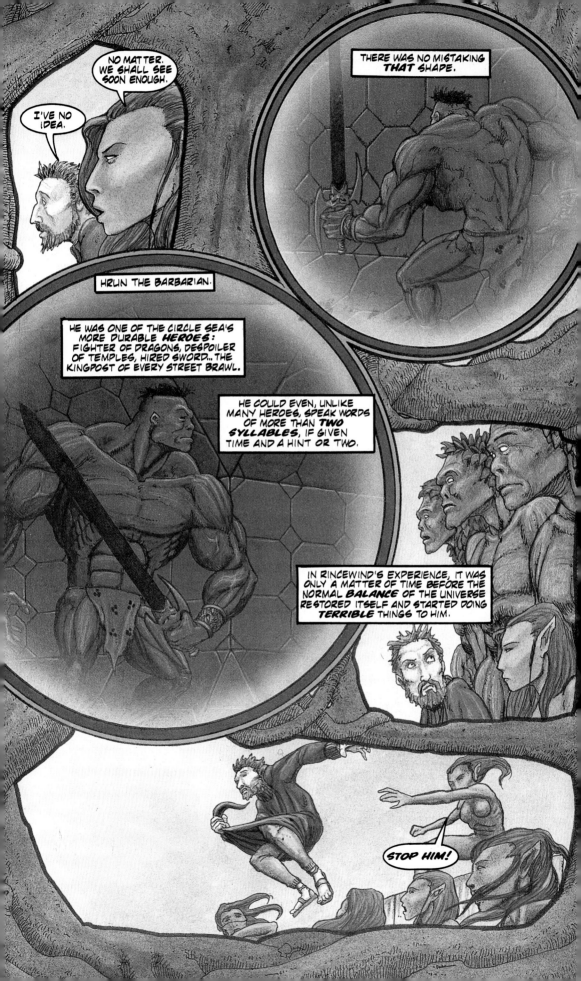

RINCEWIND KNEW THAT THE TEMPLE OF BEL-SHAMHAROTH WOULD HAVE *EIGHT* SIDES.

EIGHT WAS ALSO THE NUMBER OF BEL-SHAMHAROTH, WHICH IS WHY NO SENSIBLE WIZARD WOULD MENTION IT.

RINCEWIND'S ROOM NUMBER IN HIS RESIDENCE HALL AT THE UNSEEN UNIVERSITY HAD BEEN *7A*.

HE HADN'T BEEN SURPRISED.

THE SENDER OF EIGHT HAS *TWO* FOR DINNER IT SEEMS. WHO DOES THAT *STEED* BELONG TO, FALSE WIZARD?

IO'S OUT OF THE GAME. AT LEAST OFFLER TOOK THE *LOSS* OF THE TROLL WITH GRACE.

LADY.

LORD.

AHHH... THE SOUL OF A TRUE *HERO*.

AND NO *CHEATING*, LADY.

NO ONE. YET EVERYONE TRIES.

NOW *PLAY.*

DEPRESSING?

--I JUST MEANT THAT, I DUNNO... THINGS OUGHT TO BE MORE SORT OF *ORGANIZED*.

THE PLAIN FACT OF THE MATTER IS THAT WE'RE ON A DISC THAT IS *MANIFESTLY* TRAVERSING THE UNIVERSE ON THE BACK OF A GIANT TURTLE--

RINCEWIND THINKS HE *OUGHT* TO BE ABLE TO HARNESS THE LIGHTNING.

WHEN I SAID HARNESS, I DIDN'T MEAN *HARNESS*--

--AND THE GODS HAVE A HABIT OF GOING ROUND TO *ATHEISTS'* HOUSES AND SMASHING THEIR WINDOWS.

RATTLERATTLE
RATTLERATTLE

WOOOOSSSSHH!!

WHAT WAS THAT *NOISE?*

ARRHHH!!!

WHAT A *STRANGE* CREATURE. IS IT DANGEROUS?

ONLY TO *PEOPLE!!!*

PICTURESQUE.

THAT WAS A *NEW* WORD TO RINCEWIND THE WIZARD (B. MGC., UNSEEN UNIVERSITY [FAILED]). ONE OF A NUMBER HE HAD PICKED UP SINCE LEAVING THE *CHARRED RUINS* OF ANKH-MORPORK.

QUAINT WAS ANOTHER.

"PICTURESQUE" MEANT--

--HE DECIDED AFTER CAREFUL OBSERVATION OF THE *SCENERY* THAT INSPIRED *TWOFLOWER* TO USE THE WORD--

--HORRIBLY PRECIPITOUS.

"QUAINT", WHEN USED TO DESCRIBE THE *VILLAGES* THROUGH WHICH THEY PASSED, MEANT FEVER-RIDDEN AND TUMBLEDOWN.

TWOFLOWER WAS A *TOURIST*, THE FIRST EVER SEEN ON THE DISCWORLD. "TOURIST," RINCEWIND DECIDED, MEANT...

IDIOT!

THE SENDING OF EIGHT

ADAPTED BY: SCOTT ROCKWELL
PAINTED BY: STEVEN ROSS
LETTERED BY: VICKIE WILLIAMS
EDITED BY: DAVID CAMPITI

THERE WAS AN AIR OF CONCENTRATION AROUND THE BOARD NOW THAT THE LESSER PLAYERS HAD BEEN REMOVED FROM THE **GAME**.

RATTLE

RATTLE

CHANCE HAD BEEN AN EARLY CASUALTY, AND SHORTLY AFTERWARDS, **NIGHT** HAD CASHED IN HIS CHIPS, PLEADING AN APPOINTMENT WITH **DESTINY**.

BLIND IO TOOK UP THE DICE BOX.

CLUNK
TONK
CLUNK

SIDE BETS WERE MADE THAT **THE LADY** WOULD BE THE NEXT TO LEAVE.

A WENEGADE WIFFARD AND FOME FORT OF CLERK.

OFFLER THE CROCODILE GOD'S ACCENT WAS HINDERED, AS USUAL, BY HIS TUSKS.

THE *DISCWORLD* OFFERS SIGHTS FAR MORE IMPRESSIVE THAN THOSE FOUND IN UNIVERSES BUILT BY CREATORS WITH LESS *IMAGINATION* BUT MORE MECHANICAL APTITUDE.

PERHAPS THE MOST MAGNIFICENT SIGHT IS THE *HUB*. THERE, A SPIRE OF GREEN ICE TEN MILES HIGH RISES INTO THE CLOUDS.

AT ITS PEAK IS THE REALM OF *DUNMANIFESTIN*, THE ABODE OF THE DISC GODS.

THE DISC GODS THEMSELVES, DESPITE THE *SPLENDOR* OF THE WORLD BELOW THEM, ARE SELDOM SATISFIED.

IT IS *EMBARRASSING* TO KNOW THAT ONE IS A GOD OF A WORLD THAT ONLY EXISTS BECAUSE EVERY PROBABILITY CURVE MUST HAVE ITS FAR END.

NO WONDER THE DISC GODS SPEND MORE TIME IN *BICKERING* THAN IN OMNICOGNIZANCE.

PROLOGUE

BRBOOM WHOOOSH!

BLAST YOUR LUGGAGE! STAY HERE, AND YOU'LL GO WHERE YOU WON'T NEED LUGGAGE!

IT'S TERRIBLE! WE WERE GETTING ALONG SO WELL, TOO.

THE WINDERSHIN GATE IS THE NEAREST! COME ON!

MY LUGGAGE!

GETTING ALONG?!!

GREAT BUNCH OF FELLOWS, IT'LL BE A BLOW FOR BROADMAN. HE'D JUST PAID HIS FIRST PREMIUM.

YOU INN-SEWERED THE BROKEN DRUM?!!

OH, YES, STANDARD VALUATION. WHY DO YOU ASK?

YOU...

YOU...

RINCEWIND SEARCHED HIS MEMORY FOR THE WORST WORD IN THE TROB TONGUE. THE HAPPY LITTLE BETROBI DIDN'T REALLY KNOW HOW TO SWEAR PROPERLY.

YOU LITTLE [SUCH A ONE, WHO, WHILE WEARING A COPPER NOSE RING, STANDS IN A BATH ATOP MOUNT RARUARUAHA DURING A THUNDERSTORM AND SHOUTS THAT THE GODDESS OF LIGHTNING HAS THE FACIAL FEATURES OF A DISEASED ULORUAHA ROOT]!!!!

JUST DOING MY JOB.

LET'S GET OUT OF HERE!

IT HAS BEEN REMARKED BEFORE THAT THOSE WHO ARE SENSITIVE TO OCTARINE-- THE PIGMENT OF THE IMAGINATION--CAN SEE THINGS THAT OTHERS CANNOT.

LIKE DEATH.

I AM SURPRISED TO SEE THEE, RINCEWIND, FOR I HAVE AN APPOINTMENT WITH THEE THIS VERY NIGHT.

OH, NO! NOT--

THE VEXING THING IS THAT I WAS EXPECTING TO MEET THEE IN PERSEPOLIS. FIVE HUNDRED MILES FROM HERE.

THERE'S NO CHANCE THAT YOU COULD-- I MEAN, I COULD LEND YOU A FAST HORSE...

NOT A CHANCE!

THE WHOLE SYSTEM'S GOT SCREWED UP AGAIN.

SOD YOU, THEN. OH, WELL, ON TO THE BROKEN DRUM.

MEANWHILE, IN THE BASEMENT OF THE BROKEN DRUM...

INN-SEWER-ANTS. HUMPFF!

YOU FRET TOO MUCH, WITHEL. THE WIZARD WILL COME, HE'S TOO MUCH OF A COWARD NOT TO.

HE'LL TRY TO BARGAIN, AND WE'LL HAVE HIM. AND THE GOLD. AND THE CHEST.

WHO'D'VE THOUGHT THERE WAS THAT MUCH SAPIENT PEARWOOD ON THE WHOLE DISC?

ODD. HE DOESN'T SEEM TO REALIZE THE SERIOUSNESS OF HIS POSITION.

WHAT WAS THAT ALL ABOUT, BROADMAN?

I'M NOT REALLY SURE. IT'S A SORT OF BET, SEE? *INN-SEWER-ANTS.* IT'S LIKE A BET THAT THE BROKEN DRUM WON'T BURN DOWN.

THIS WORM-EATEN TINDER PILE? HE MUST BE MAD!

THEY MUST HAVE TAKEN HIM TO THE BROKEN DRUM. I'LL HAVE TO--

OOOOFF! WATCH WHERE YOU'RE--

--GOING?

RINCEWIND?

SINCE THEN, IT HAD BEEN SHOWING A WORRYING TENDENCY, WHEN RINCEWIND WAS ESPECIALLY RUNDOWN OR THREATENED--

--TO GET ITSELF SAID.

CRASH-SCREEEEECH!

THE SPELL DIED, UNSAID.

♪

SHOO.

LOOK, YOU'VE GOT THE WRONG MAN. I DIDN'T KIDNAP HIM!

tap tap tap tap tap...

IT WON'T STOP UNTIL YOU GIVE IN, YOU KNOW. YOU'RE A WIZARD. YOU'LL THINK OF SOME WAY TO FIND HIM.

NOT MUCH OF A WIZARD. I ONLY KNOW ONE SPELL. AND FRANKLY--

--NO SPELLS ARE MUCH GOOD. IT TAKES THREE MONTHS TO COMMIT EVEN A SIMPLE SPELL TO MEMORY, THEN ONCE YOU'VE USED IT, POOF! IT'S GONE.

WHEN TWOFLOWER SAID THEY HAD A BETTER KIND OF MAGIC CALLED REFLECTED-SOUND-OF-UNDERGROUND SPIRITS, I THOUGHT...

...I THOUGHT HE MEANT A BETTER WAY OF DOING THINGS... SOMETHING WITH A BIT OF SENSE IN IT. HARNESSING THE LIGHTNING, I SUPPOSE.

EVEN IF YOU COULD GET A HARNESS ON IT, HOW COULD YOU GET IT TO PULL A CART? IT'D PROBABLY BURN THROUGH THE HARNESS, ANYWAY.

CREEAAKK!!

ALL RIGHT! ALL RIGHT! I'M THINKING!

IT IS PERHAPS UNTRUE TO SAY THAT RINCEWIND HAD LEARNED THE SPELL. IT HAD LEARNED HIM.

THE EPISODE HAD LED TO HIS EXPULSION FROM THE UNSEEN UNIVERSITY, BECAUSE, FOR A BET--

--HE HAD DARED TO OPEN THE LAST REMAINING COPY OF THE CREATOR'S OWN GRIMOIRE, THE *OCTAVO*.

THE SPELL HAD LEAPT OUT OF THE PAGE AND BURROWED DEEPLY INTO RINCEWIND'S MIND--

--FROM WHENCE THE COMBINED TALENTS OF THE FACULTY OF MEDICINE HAD BEEN UNABLE TO COAX IT.

PRECISELY WHICH OF THE SPELLS IT WAS, THEY WERE UNABLE TO ASCERTAIN, EXCEPT THAT IT WAS ONE OF THE EIGHT BASIC SPELLS.

THE BASIC SPELLS THAT WERE INTRICATELY INTERWOVEN INTO THE FABRIC OF TIME AND SPACE ITSELF.

CLICK!

IT'S NO GOOD. I'VE RUN OUT OF PINK.

NO PINK! SEE? IF YOU WANTED PINK, THEN YOU SHOULDN'T HAVE TAKEN ALL THOSE PICTURES OF THE YOUNG LADIES, SHOULD YOU?

IT'S MONOCHROME FROM NOW ON, FRIEND. ALRIGHT?

ALRIGHT. YEAH. SURE.

UHH, TWOFLOWER--

SLAM!

TWOFLOWER?!!

TURN WITHOUT HASTE.

OR KISS YOUR KIDNEYS GOODBYE.

A PROLONGED SESSION AT THE WHORE PITS PRODUCED A NUMBER OF COLORFUL AND INSTRUCTIVE PICTURES--

--SEVERAL OF WHICH RINCEWIND CONCEALED ABOUT HIS PERSON FOR DETAILED PERUSAL IN PRIVATE.

EVEN A FAILED WIZARD KNEW THAT SOME SUBSTANCES WERE SENSITIVE TO LIGHT. PERHAPS THE SQUARE BITS OF PAPER WERE TREATED BY SOME ARCANE PROCESS THAT FROZE THE LIGHT THAT PASSED THROUGH THEM.

HE NOTICED SOMETHING ELSE STRANGE-- POSSESSION OF THE BOX CONFERRED A KIND OF POWER ON THE WIELDER--

--ANYONE, CONFRONTED WITH THE HYPNOTIC GLASS EYE, WOULD SUBMISSIVELY OBEY THE MOST PEREMPTORY ORDERS ABOUT STANCE AND EXPRESSION.

IT WAS WHILE HE WAS THUS ENGAGED IN THE PLAZA OF THE BROKEN MOON THAT DISASTER STRUCK.

SOMETIME LATER, AFTER LUNCH AND WINE HAD DONE MUCH TO RELAX RINCEWIND...

TAVERN FIGHTS ARE PRETTY COMMON AROUND HERE, I EXPECT? NO DOUBT THE FIXTURES AND FITTINGS GET DAMAGED.

FIXT-- OH, I SEE. THE BENCHES AND WHATNOT, I SUPPOSE SO.

I MIGHT BE ABLE TO HELP THERE. RISKS ARE MY BUSINESS.

YOU TAKE RISKS?

OH, NO. I ASSESS THEM. DO YOU KNOW WHAT THE ODDS ARE OF A HOUSE CATCHING FIRE IN THE RED TRIANGLE DISTRICT OF BES PELARGIC? FIVE HUNDRED THIRTY EIGHT TO ONE.

I CALCULATED THAT.

WHAT-- URP-- WHAT FOR? 'SCUSE ME.

FOR-- I CAN'T SAY IT IN TROB. IN MY LANGUAGE WE CALL IT-- INN-SEWER-ANTS.

I WORK OUT THE ODDS AGAINST BAD THINGS HAPPENING, ADD A BIT, THEN YOU PAY ME SOME MONEY BASED ON THOSE ODDS.

THEN, IF SOMETHING BAD DOES HAPPEN, I REIMBURSE YOU.

I DON' UNNERSTAN' THIS INN-SEWER-ANTS. MAGIC, NOW. MAGIC I UNNERSTAN'.

WELL, MAGIC IS ONE THING, AND REFLECTED-SOUND-OF-UNDERGROUND SPIRITS IS ANOTHER.

REFLECTED-SOUND-OF-UNDERGROUND-SPIRITS? NEVER HEARD O' IT.

TWOFLOWER TRIED TO EXPLAIN.

RINCEWIND TRIED TO UNDERSTAND.

YARGH!

WOOOOSSSSHHHH!!

PROBABLY A LUCKY THROW. THEY ALL SEEM TOO BUSY TO NOTICE ME.

LUCKILY, IN THE RAGING GLOOM NO ONE SEEMED TO NOTICE A SHADOWY SHAPE THAT SHUFFLED FROM TABLE TO TABLE TOWARD THE STAIRWAY.

ONE SUCH LETTER ARRIVED THIS MORNING. A SUBJECT OF THE EMPEROR HAS TAKEN IT IN HIS HEAD TO VISIT OUR CITY.

ONLY A MADMAN WOULD UNDERGO THE PRIVATIONS OF CROSSING THE TURNWISE OCEAN IN ORDER MERELY TO LOOK AT ANYTHING. HOWEVER.

HE LANDED THIS MORNING. HE MIGHT HAVE MET A GREAT HERO, OR SOME WISE SAGE. HE MET YOU.

YOU WILL SEE THAT HE RETURNS HOME WITH A GOOD REPORT OF OUR LITTLE HOMELAND. WHAT DO YOU SAY TO THAT?

ER, THANK YOU, LORD.

IT WOULD BE A TRAGEDY SHOULD ANYTHING UNTOWARD HAPPEN TO OUR VISITOR. THE AGATEAN EMPEROR LOOKS AFTER HIS OWN AND COULD EXTINGUISH US WITH A NOD.

BUT IN THE WEEKS BEFORE THE AGATEAN FLEET ARRIVED, MY SERVANTS WOULD OCCUPY THEMSELVES ABOUT YOUR PERSON...

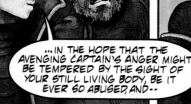

...IN THE HOPE THAT THE AVENGING CAPTAIN'S ANGER MIGHT BE TEMPERED BY THE SIGHT OF YOUR STILL LIVING BODY, BE IT EVER SO ABUSED, AND--

BUT I SEE YOU UNDERSTAND.

YES, LORD. I'LL, ER... LOOK AFTER HIM AND SEE HE COMES TO NO HARM.

AND THEN I'LL GET A JOB JUGGLING SNOWBALLS IN HELL.

"...A CONTINENT WHICH, THOUGH SMALL, IS OF AN EQUAL WEIGHT TO ALL THE MIGHTY LAND MASSES OF OUR HEMI-CIRCLE?"

"AND THAT THIS, ACCORDING TO ANCIENT LEGEND, IS BECAUSE IT IS MADE LARGELY OF GOLD?"

WHO HASN'T HEARD OF THE COUNTERWEIGHT CONTINENT? SOME SAILORS HAVE EVEN BELIEVED THE CHILDHOOD TALES AND SAILED IN SEARCH OF IT.

IT DOES, OF COURSE, EXIST. IT IS NOT MADE OF GOLD, BUT GOLD IS VERY COMMON THERE. MOST OF THE MASS IS MADE UP OF VAST OCTIRON DEPOSITS DEEP WITHIN THE CRUST.

"I MAY AS WELL TELL YOU, RINCEWIND, THAT THERE IS SOME VERY SLIGHT CONTACT BETWEEN THE LORDS OF THE CIRCLE SEA AND THE EMPEROR OF THE AGATEAN EMPIRE.

"THERE IS LITTLE COMMON GROUND BETWEEN US. WE HAVE NOTHING THEY WANT, AND THEY HAVE NOTHING WE CAN AFFORD.

"SO WE EXCHANGE FRATERNAL GREETINGS BY ALBATROSS MAIL.

"AT INFREQUENT INTERVALS,"

[ME? RICH? I AM BUT A POOR CLERK! WHATEVER GAVE YOU THE IDEA THAT I WAS *RICH*?]

[YOU HAVE, UH... GOLD.]

[BARELY TWO THOUSAND *RHINU*. HARDLY ENOUGH TO KEEP A MAN ALIVE FOR A MONTH OR TWO AT HOME.]

[AN *IDEA* OCCURS TO ME, RINCEWIND, WOULD YOU CONSENT TO BE EMPLOYED AS A, I DON'T KNOW... GUIDE? I THINK I COULD AFFORD TO PAY A RHINU A DAY... OR ONE AND ONE-HALF RHINU?]

CAN I SHOW YOU TO YOUR *ROOM*, SIR?

RINCEWIND WAS TO CALL BACK AT *NOON* TO SHOW TWOFLOWER AROUND THE CITY.

TWOFLOWER HAD *INSISTED* ON PAYING HIS FIRST FOUR DAYS WAGES IN ADVANCE.

AS A STUDENT, RINCEWIND HAD NEVER RECEIVED HIGH MARKS IN PRECOGNITION, BUT NOW, UNUSED CIRCUITS IN HIS BRAIN WERE THROBBING OUT THE FUTURE.

THE *SENSIBLE* THING TO DO WOULD BE TO BUY A *HORSE*...

BUT WHAT WILL HAPPEN TO TWOFLOWER, ALONE IN A CITY WHERE EVEN THE COCKROACHES HAVE AN UNERRING INSTINCT FOR GOLD?

A MAN WOULD HAVE TO BE A REAL *HEEL* TO LEAVE HIM.

THE SPACE BETWEEN HIS SHOULDER BLADES BEGAN TO ITCH.

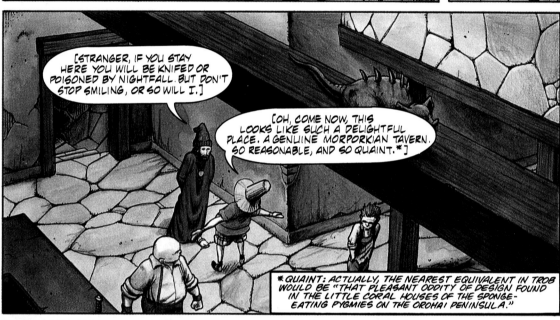

MAY I BE OF ASSISTANCE? I HAVE AN INNATE GIFT FOR *LANGUAGES*.

SHOVE *OFF*, RINCEWIND.

FOOOOOD. CUTLET, HASH, STEW, RAGOUT, FRICASEE, SORBET, SOUFFLE, SAUSAGE, NOT TO HAVE A SAUSAGE, JELLY, JAM...

I ONLY THOUGHT IT MIGHT BE *USEFUL* TO ADDRESS THIS GENTLEMAN IN HIS OWN TONGUE.

RINCEWIND TRIED A FEW WORDS OF *CHIMERAN*.

HE SWITCHED TO *HIGH BOROGRAVIAN*...

VANGLEMESHT...

EVEN *BLACK OROOGU*, A LANGUAGE WITH NO NOUNS AND ONLY ONE ADJECTIVE, WHICH IS OBSCENE...

IN DESPERATION, HE TRIED *HEATHEN TROB*.

[AT LAST! MY GOOD SIR! THIS IS REMARKABLE*]

* OR, IN *TROB*; "A THING WHICH MAY HAPPEN BUT ONCE IN THE USABLE LIFETIME OF A CANOE HOLLOWED DILIGENTLY BY AXE AND FIRE FROM THE TALLEST TREE ON THE SLOPES OF MOUNT AWAYAYA, HOME OF THE FIREGODS OR SO IT IS SAID."

HOW CAN A BOOK TELL A MAN WHAT TO SAY? AND WHAT THE HELL'S *THAT*?

JUST DON'T TALK ABOUT IT, BROADMAN.

I WISH FOR AN ACCOMODATION, A ROOM, LODGINGS, THE LODGING HOUSE, FULL BOARD, ARE YOUR ROOMS CLEAN, A ROOM WITH A VIEW, WHAT IS YOUR RATE FOR ONE NIGHT?

ALL EYES IN THE BROKEN DRUM AT THAT MOMENT WATCHED THE *STRANGER*--

--EXCEPT FOR A PAIR BELONGING TO RINCEWIND, THE WIZARD.

SOME *MIGHT* HAVE TAKEN HIM FOR A MERE APPRENTICE ENCHANTER WHO HAD RUN AWAY FROM HIS MASTER OUT OF DEFIANCE, BOREDOM, AND A LINGERING TASTE FOR HETEROSEXUALITY.

YET HE WEARS THE BRONZE OCTAGON OF THE UNSEEN UNIVERSITY, THE HIGH SCHOOL OF *MAGIC* ON THE DISC.

RINCEWIND WAS STARING AT THE LUGGAGE.

SAPIENT PEARWOOD!

AN ARCHMAGE, BY DINT OF GREAT EFFORT, MIGHT SOMEDAY OBTAIN A SMALL STAFF MADE FROM THE TIMBER OF A SAPIENT PEARTREE.

IT GREW *ONLY* ON THE SITES OF ANCIENT MAGIC.

RINCEWIND TRIED TO CALCULATE ITS *VALUE*.

A *VEIN* BEGAN TO THROB IN HIS *FOREHEAD*.

ODD.

HE HAD THIS BIG WOODEN *CHEST,* YMOR.

HE'D HAVE TO BE A MERCHANT OR A SPY. WHAT DO YOU THINK, WITHEL?

I'VE CHECKED ON THE SHIP. IT'S A FREE-LANCE TRADER. DOES RUNS TO THE BROWN ISLANDS. PEOPLE THERE ARE SAVAGES.

THEY DON'T UNDERSTAND ABOUT SPIES AND I EXPECT THEY *EAT* MERCHANTS.

AH... OUR MESSAGE FROM GORRIN THE CAT. HE'S STATIONED ON THE GONG TOWER OF THE *TEMPLE OF SMALL GODS.*

HUGH HAS TAKEN OUR STRANGER TO THE BROKEN DRUM... GORRIN MUST HAVE BEEN A CUSTOMER THERE RECENTLY, FOR HE WRITES OF A BOX ON LEGS...

HE WILL BE *DISCIPLINED.*

DAMN! HE OWED ME THREE COPPER PIECES.

I THINK WE'LL WANDER ALONG TO THE DRUM *LATER ON,* WITHEL.

THE **HUB** OF THE DISCWORLD IS NEVER CLOSELY WARMED BY THE WEAK SUN AND THE LANDS THERE ARE LOCKED IN **PERMAFROST**.

THE **RIM**, ON THE OTHER HAND, IS A REGION OF **SUNNY ISLANDS** AND **BALMY DAYS**.

THERE ARE **EIGHT DAYS** IN A DISC WEEK AND **EIGHT COLOURS** IN ITS LIGHT SPECTRUM. EIGHT IS A NUMBER OF SOME CONSIDERABLE **OCCULT SIGNIFICANCE** ON THE DISC.

PRECISELY **WHY** ALL THIS SHOULD BE SO IS NOT CLEAR-- BUT IT **DOES** GO SOME WAY TO EXPLAIN WHY, ON THE DISC, THE GODS ARE NOT SO MUCH WORSHIPPED, AS **BLAMED**.

THE TWIN CITY OF **ANKH MORPORK**, OF WHICH ALL OTHER CITIES OF TIME AND SPACE ARE, AS IT WERE, MERE **REFLECTIONS**.

PROUD **ANKH** AND PESTILENT **MORPORK** HAVE STOOD MANY ASSAULTS IN THEIR LONG AND CROWDED TWIN HISTORY, AND HAVE ALWAYS RISEN TO FLOURISH AGAIN...

...SO THE FIRE AND ITS SUBSEQUENT FLOOD THAT WILL HAPPEN SOON WILL **NOT** MARK ITS END--

--BUT RATHER BE MERELY A FIERY PUNCTUATION MARK, A COAL-LIKE COMMA, OR SALAMANDER SEMICOLON IN A **CONTINUING** STORY.